Written by Ian MacDonald

Illustrated by Michael Emmerson

I'm not scared. Are you scared?
No, I'm not scared at all.
Just Tom and Oscar in our tent,
out by the garden wall.

We're tucked up in our sleeping bags,
in our tent out on the lawn.
With my teddy and my blanket,
as Oscar starts to yawn.

But hush, is that a bear we hear
padding by our door?
It's got a snorting nose and scary eyes,
sharp teeth and great big paws!

“Mummy, help us, please.
We think a bear is after us!”
“Hush now, dears, it’s not a bear.
Now don’t make such a fuss.”

"It was just a fox you saw,
so settle down and sleep.
Just a fox snuffling round our bins.
Now, not another peep!"

I'm not scared. Are you scared?
No, I'm not scared one bit.
Tonight we're sleeping in our tent
and we're glad the lamp is lit!

But what is that we hear,
like a whisper in the night?
Pale shapes flapping in the dark ...
two phantoms, spooky white!

"Help Mum, there's spooks after us!
We know there's something there."
"Quiet, dear, it's nothing spooky
that's given you a scare."

"Just the washing on the line,
Dad's shirt and my white shawl,
flapping in the evening breeze.
That's what you saw, that's all!"

I'm not scared. Are you scared?
No, I'm as brave as I can be.
Tonight we're sleeping in our tent,
outside, just you and me.

But wait, is that a serpent?
A snake we think we saw!
It's hissing and slithering across the lawn,
with sharp fangs and open jaws.

"It came sliding to our tent, Mum!
It gave us such a scare."
"Hush dears, it's not a snake you see.
Just take a look out there."

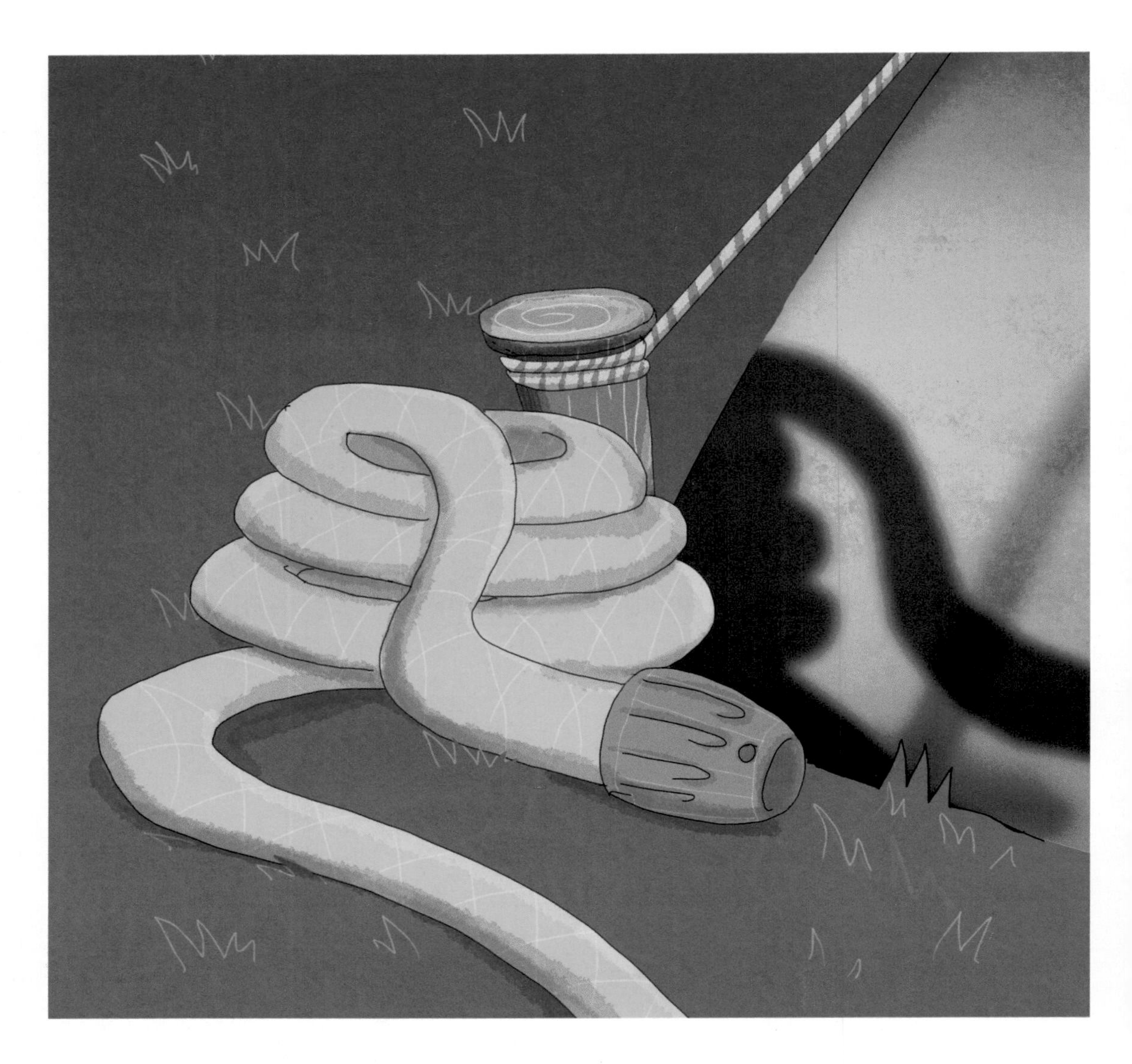

"Look, it's just the garden hose
left outside on the lawn.
So take care now, go back to bed
before night turns to dawn!"

I'm not scared. Are you scared?
No, not even if we're alone.
As tonight we are both sleeping
outside our nice, warm home.

Oh no! I hear another sound ...
the rattling of old bones.
A skeleton by the garden gate,
click-clacking on the stones.

It has a snapping jaw, chattering teeth,
and two vast eyes that stare!
"It's not a skeleton, Tom and Oscar.
Come take a look, if you dare."

"It's just the wind blowing a pipe
that's swinging against the wall.
It's clattering on the bare bricks.
There's nothing to be afraid of at all!"

I’m not scared. Are you scared?
No, we’re safe from all our fears,
tucked up in our living room.
“Goodnight, sweet dreams, my dears!”

Talk about the story

Answer the questions:

1 What were the boys' names?

2 Where were they sleeping?

3 Why did the boys feel scared?

4 Was there really a snake outside the tent?

5 Have you ever slept in a tent? What was it like?

6 Are you ever scared of the dark?

Can you retell the story in your own words?